Alien Tea
on Planet Zum-Zee

You are invited to:
the greatest party in the universe!
Make your way to planet Zum-Zee,
and try some terrifically tasty treats
from outer space.

Don't be late!

To Emer and Cormac, with best wishes – T.M.

To Jack and Zoe, with love – G.P-R.

ORCHARD BOOKS   First published in Great Britain in 2011 by Orchard Books   This edition published in 2016 by The Watts Publishing Group

The moral rights of the author and illustrator have been asserted.   All rights reserved.   A CIP catalogue record for this book is available from the British Library.

An imprint of   Hachette Children's Group   Part of The Watts Publishing Group Limited

Carmelite House   50 Victoria Embankment   London EC4Y 0DZ   An Hachette UK Company   www.hachette.co.uk   www.hachettechildrens.co.uk

10 9 8 7 6 5 4 3 2 1   Text © Tony Mitton, 2011   Illustrations © Guy Parker-Rees, 2011   ISBN 978 1 40834 691 4   Printed and bound in China   Orchard Books

Alien Tea
on Planet Zum-Zee

Tony Mitton
Guy Parker-Rees

ORCHARD

If you take your rocket to the outer edge of space,
you'll come across a funny little alien place.

The alien peoples call it **Planet Zum-Zee**,
and they're meeting here today for a special picnic tea.

It seems really quiet and there's no one around. But, hey! Just a minute. Now, **what's that sound?**

Zakka-
Zakka-
Zakka!

Now, what's this here?
A crazy kind of capsule
is beginning to appear.

A door slides open
with a **click**
and a ***whirr,***

and out come
creatures
all covered
with fur.

They're jolly and they're **yellow**,
and they're carrying a **cake**.
It **wiggles** and it **giggles**
when they give it a shake.

It's an Alien Party on Planet Zum-Zee,
so bring along some goodies for the Alien Tea.

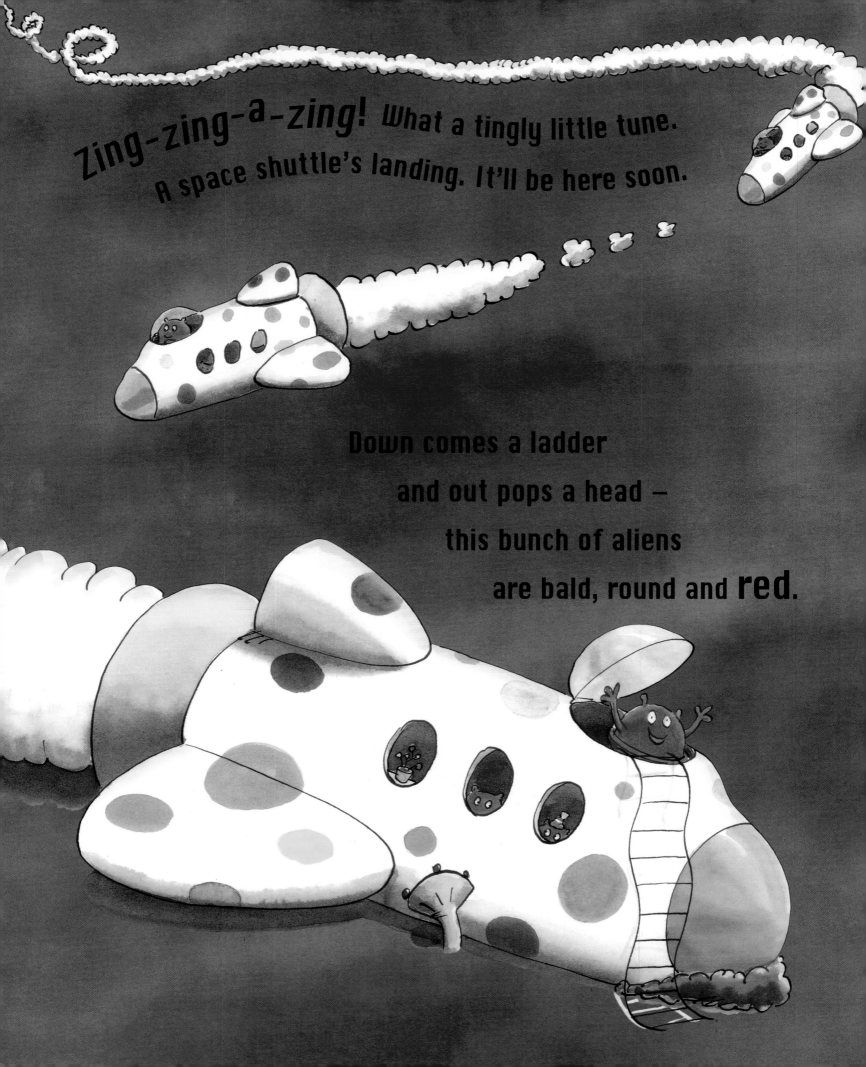

Zing-zing-a-zing! What a tingly little tune.
A space shuttle's landing. It'll be here soon.

Down comes a ladder
and out pops a head –
this bunch of aliens
are bald, round and red.

He **huffs** and he **hurries.**

He can see that **he's late.**

Here he comes, puffing, with a **big, round plate.**

It's loaded with **dollops**, all gloopy and **blue**.
They **quiver** and they **shiver** like rubbery goo.

They're **humming** and they're **glowing** like magical jelly, and **hissing** with steam which is **purple** and **smelly**.

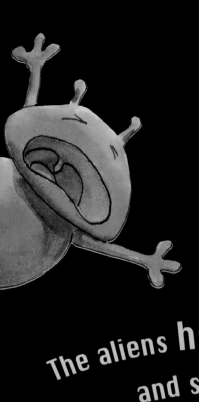
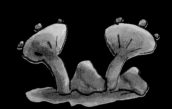

The aliens **holler,**
and some hold their **nose,**

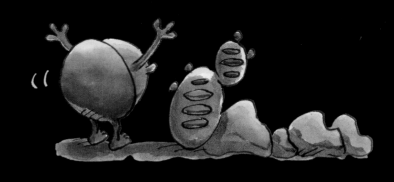

some **shake** their **bottoms**, and some **wave** their **toes**,

then they all **shout** together . . .

eating those!"

Poor old Monster,
he's sliding away,
but as he wobbles off,
what's happening?

Hey!

One little alien, bald, round and red,
scuttles to the plate, then **swivels** his head.
He sticks out a feeler
to give the gloop a prod.

He picks it and licks it –
he's starting to nod.

He scoops it and slurps it,
then gives a long sigh . . .

Quickly, the others come whiffling around.
They start to dip in with a dollopy sound.

It looks a bit yucky as it sits on the plate.

It's **gloppy**, it's **gloopy**, but it tastes just great!

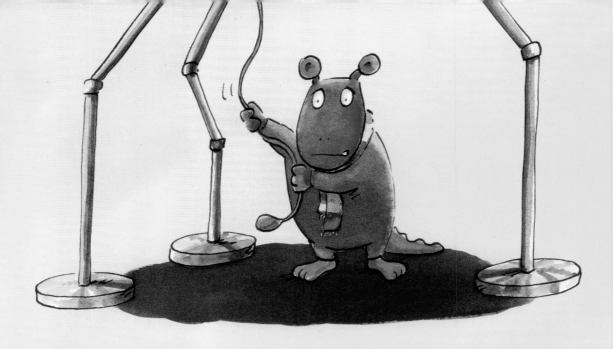

The little red alien
bleeps a loud shout,

"Hey there, Monster!
Don't be left out!
Come back and party. Stay here with us.
We're sorry we hurt you
by making a fuss."

Monster cheers up, and he wobbles their way.
They jump up and down and they all cheer,
"Yay!"

. . . it's the **alien**

mummies!

They warble goodbyes with a burble and bleep.
It's getting near bedtime. They'll soon need their sleep.

And no one would guess,
if they came to Zum-Zee,

that this was the home of the Alien Tea.